COMMUNICATION

FACTS ● THINGS TO MAKE ● ACTIVITIES

TING MORRIS
Illustrated by Ed Dovey

Watts Books
London ● New York ● Sydney

© Watts Books 1995

Watts Books
96 Leonard Street
London EC2A 4RH

Franklin Watts
14 Mars Road
Lane Cove
NSW 2066

UK ISBN: 0 7496 1871 X

10 9 8 7 6 5 4 3 2 1

Editor: Annabel Martin
Designed by: Sally Boothroyd
Consultants: Roy Fancourt and Carole Stacey
Photography by: Martyn Chillmaid
Additional picture research by: Veneta Bullen
Models made by: Emma and Sam Morris

Dewey Decimal Classification: 302.2

A CIP catalogue record for this book is available from
the British Library.

Printed in the United Kingdom

CONTENTS

COMMUNICATION

Communication is the passing on of information from one person to another. Human beings, along with many animals, communicate with each other all the time. The word communicate comes from a Latin word that means "to share". When we communicate with other people, we share ideas or information with them.

To communicate something to our friends, we usually talk to them. Speech is the most useful and important way of making contact with people, though the human race does not share a common language. Throughout history humans have shown a wish to communicate with those around them as well as over longer distances.

c. 20000 B.C. cave paintings/ smoke signals

c. 2800 B.C. Egyptian hieroglyphics

500 B.C. Greek beacon fires

A.D. 105 Chinese invent paper

1456 Johannes Gutenberg prints the first book using movable metal type

c. 3100 B.C. pictographic writing; picture symbols

1200 B.C. Chinese logograms

59 B.C. Greeks write on wax tablets; Romans produce Acta Diurna, first handwritten news sheet

868 Chinese invent printing

HISTORY OF COMMUNICATION

Over the centuries, means of communication have developed from primitive drum signals to satellite networks that provide global communication. People have gradually devised more and more ingenious ways of communicating, from growls, dances and disguises to smoke signals, flags and coded messages. Today books, newspapers and magazines, the telephone and fax, radio and television all help people to stay in touch. Recent developments in computer technology have played an enormous part in personal and mass communication.

Without effective forms of communication knowledge could not be passed from generation to generation. There would be no record of the past, no books and no shared knowledge for future generations to use. People would have to find out about the world for themselves.

HIGHLIGHTS IN THE HISTORY OF COMMUNICATION

This timechart shows how communication developed from cave paintings to the modern systems we use today.

1838 Samuel Morse invents Morse Code

1876 Alexander Graham Bell invents telephone

1926 John Logie Baird invents television

1956 video recorder invented

1474 William Caxton starts his printing press

1868 Americans invent typewriter

1901 Guglielmo Marconi sends first radio signal across Atlantic

1945 world's first computer

1977 world's first glass-fibre cable telephone link

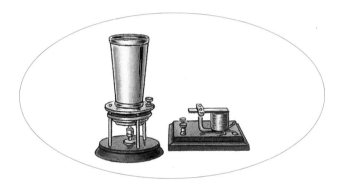

PASSING ON MESSAGES

People use their brains and the five senses to pass on and receive information. The brain contains billions of nerve cells and is involved in everything that we do. Nerves carry instructions from our brains to our bodies and from our body's sense organs back to our brains. The brain monitors all these signals and helps us to learn by storing memories.

We frequently use speech to communicate, but spoken words only last for a second and cannot be heard far away. Therefore we have learned to communicate at a distance using written language, which also means knowledge can be saved for the future. Speech and writing both use words, but there are other ways of passing on information.

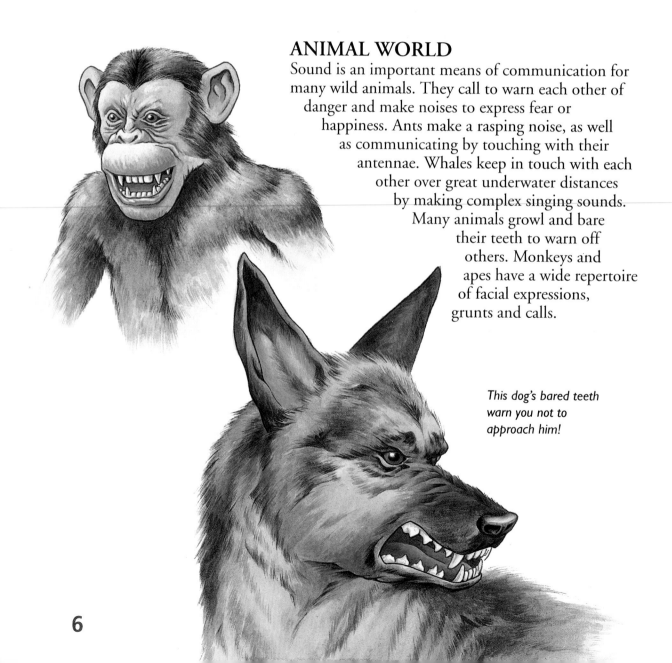

ANIMAL WORLD

Sound is an important means of communication for many wild animals. They call to warn each other of danger and make noises to express fear or happiness. Ants make a rasping noise, as well as communicating by touching with their antennae. Whales keep in touch with each other over great underwater distances by making complex singing sounds. Many animals growl and bare their teeth to warn off others. Monkeys and apes have a wide repertoire of facial expressions, grunts and calls.

This dog's bared teeth warn you not to approach him!

SIGNS AND GESTURES

Our early ancestors probably used signs to communicate. For example, a gliding movement of the hand might have told a fellow hunter that there was a snake nearby. Today, we wave our hand to say goodbye to someone.

North American Indian tribes communicated by sign language because their spoken languages were different. Some hand signals were understood by all the different tribes and were later learned by white trappers and European explorers.

Hello

See

Listen

Friend

Yes

No

Cry

Speak

Ashamed

Meet

Bear

Baby

Tell a story to a friend, using sign language. You could use some Indian signs and make up your own signals, sounds and movements to act out the story.

7

BODY LANGUAGE

You can usually tell a lot about how people are feeling from the expressions on their faces and the gestures they make. Body language is used to communicate messages without words. Happiness is expressed by a smile, anger by a scowl; a person will blush when embarrassed and cry when sad. A shake of the head, a shrug of the shoulders and a wave of the hand are all part of our body language. Very often we make these signals without thinking – they are unconscious acts.

Certain signals, such as smiling, laughing or crying, are understood without fail among people everywhere

SPORTING SIGNALS

In many sports, team members need to communicate quickly and effectively. A soccer player might point to show where he would like the ball played. Rugby players use their own number or word code to let their team know where the ball will be thrown at a line-out. American football teams have complex systems of numbers, words and signals to tell their players what the next play will be. In many sports the referee also uses hand signals to communicate his decisions to players and spectators.

MIME

Body language has developed into a special art form in the theatre. A mime artist uses gestures and bodily movements to act out a story without using words. Mime can be traced back to the days when early humans used it to re-enact successful hunts or battles.

DANCE

All over the world, people use dance to tell stories and display emotions. Many celebrations take the form of dance. At a modern disco, dancers express their own feelings and the mood of the music through body language.

Ballet dancing is a beautiful form of communication

CHARADES

Charades is a popular miming game for two or more players. One player chooses the title of a well-known book, play, film or television programme. Then he or she acts out the chosen title without speaking. Only actions and gestures are allowed. The player can break the title down into separate words or syllables and act them out in order. When someone guesses the title correctly it is their turn to mime a title. Certain gestures have become standard in charades, to make the game quicker and easier.

Book

Film

Play

TV Programme

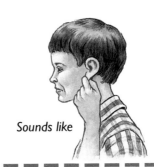

Sounds like

AT A GLANCE

We tell each other things by the way we look and dress.

BODY PAINTING

Decorating the body with pictures and designs is an ancient custom. Paints and dyes can be washed off and were usually only put on for special occasions. Many North American Indian tribes painted their faces and bodies with elaborate designs. Certain colours indicated membership of a particular group or society. When Indian warriors prepared for battle, they applied war paint to look fierce and strong.

Above: *A Sioux Indian warrior wearing white war paint*

Below: *A member of the Maori tribe with face tattoos*

Tattoos are used in a similar way, but they are permanent decorations. Tattoos have often been used to show a person's position in a tribe or society, or to indicate a great achievement or a religious belief. Many people of the Pacific Islands believed that tattooing made them look more beautiful and courageous. Among the Maori of New Zealand, the more important an individual was, the more tattoos he or she had. Maori chiefs sometimes had their faces completely covered in tattoos.

YOU ARE WHAT YOU WEAR

The make-up, jewellery and clothes you wear are a form of language too. They tell people things about you. A football supporter's replica shirt or a baseball fan's cap show others which team they support. In the same way, professional uniforms tell people at a glance who they are dealing with. A police officer's uniform and a nurse's outfit are unmistakable, and recognising them in an emergency may help save lives.

People wear particular clothes for occasions such as weddings and funerals. But different cultures and religions have developed different traditions. Muslim brides dress in bright colours. Chinese brides wear dragon designs to bring them good luck.

MASKS AND DRAGONS

Masks have played an important part in many cultures. Their main message is to warn off evil intruders from the spirit world.

The Chinese dragon is thought to be lucky and full of energy. Its mask has bulging eyes and a gaping mouth. Huge dragons take part in street processions at Chinese New Year, to symbolize good luck, strength and energy. Their bodies are made from lengths of bamboo covered with coloured cloth. Some dragons are over 30 metres long and need 50 people to help them twist and turn through the streets.

Chinese dragon dancers

Make a fabulous Chinese dragon, symbol of strength and good luck.

MAKING THE MASK

1. Cut off the bottom flaps of the big box and tape the sides up. Shape the sides to fit over your shoulders. Cut out a peephole slit to see through. Tape the smaller box on top of the big box. Make sure you leave a ledge at least 6 cm wide at the front of the two boxes for the mouth to fit on.

You will need: ● big cardboard box to fit your head and shoulders ● slightly smaller cardboard box to go on top ● 3 metres string ● parcel tape ● cardboard ● half a packet of wallpaper paste ● brushes, scissors, bowl ● glue ● red, yellow, black and white poster paints, green ready-mixed paint ● red, yellow and white strong paper ● glitter or glitter glue ● newspaper ● 2 wash balls ● plate to draw round

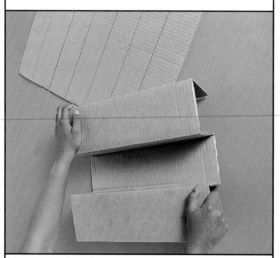

▲ 2. The mouth: Use a strip of cardboard as wide as the top box and 70 cm long. Divide the cardboard strip into seven 10 cm sections by drawing six straight lines on it. Score the cardboard along these lines with the tip of your scissors. Fold the card along the scored lines to make a mouth with an upper and a lower jaw. Tape the mouth to the boxes, with the fifth section – the lower jaw – resting on the ledge.

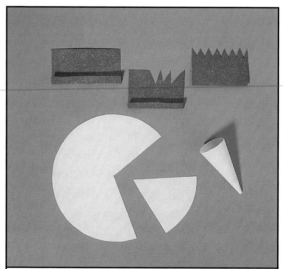

▲ 3. For eyes, tape two wash balls above the mouth. For the head frills, cut three 15-cm wide red paper strips. Zig-zag one side and make a 2-cm fold on the other. Tape the folded edges to the top and sides of the box. For the horns, draw around a large plate. Cut a segment out of the paper circle, and roll the remaining circle into a cone. Fix the cones to the box with tape.

▲ **4.** Tear newspaper into strips, about 3 cm wide. Mix the wallpaper paste according to the instructions on the packet and coat the strips with it. Cover the boxes, mouth and eyes with two layers of paste-covered paper. Leave the mask to dry overnight.

▲ **5.** When the mask is dry, paint it green. Paint the inside of the mouth red. Use poster paints to give your dragon fiery eyes. Add glitter for extra sparkle. When the head is dry, cut four white paper strips for teeth, serrate the edges, and make a fold to glue them on. Don't forget the nostrils!

6. Decorate the neck with glittering crêpe-paper strips. Finally, pierce two holes 6 cm from the bottom and the sides at the back and front of the mask for the string. Cut the string in half and thread one piece through the front and the other through the holes at the back. Now you can tie the mask on. Cross over the front strings and tie them at the back. Do the same with the back strings.

DOING THE DRAGON TWIST

Get together with a few friends and make a long dragon. For its body, decorate an old sheet or curtain with zig-zag edges and scaly markings. The leader wears the mask and puts the sheet over his/her shoulders like a cloak, fastening it with a safety pin under the neck. The dragon bearers stand in line with their heads bowed, holding on to the hips of the person in front. The sheet is draped over them and the dance can begin. To twist and turn like a dragon, everyone must walk on the same foot in time with each other.

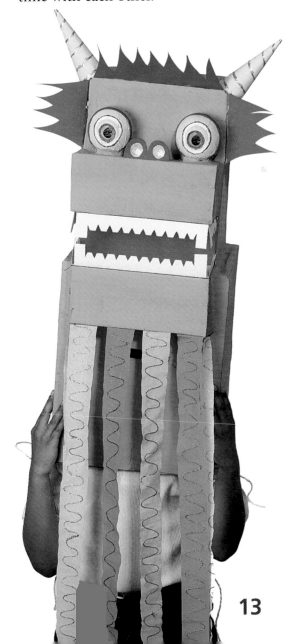

13

LONG-DISTANCE INFORMATION

In earliest times, people had no way of communicating their knowledge to people thousands of kilometres away. Over the centuries, many different methods of long-distance communication have been used.

FIRE AND SMOKE

One of the earliest methods of signalling was to light a fire on high ground and use it as a beacon. The ancient Chinese, Egyptians and Persians all used beacons. These were often lit on a series of hills, each one visible from the next. Over 3000 years ago, a chain of beacons informed the people of Argos in Greece that the city of Troy had been destroyed.

The same method was still used in 1588, when people in England were warned that the Spanish Armada had been sighted off the south coast.

North American Indians used fires to send smoke signals. They waved blankets over a fire to produce puffs of smoke. The smoke signals had a special coded meaning, so that Indians watching far away could understand the message.

FLASHING LIGHTS

As early as the 5th century B.C., the ancient Greeks passed messages by reflecting sunlight in polished metal mirrors. Before the introduction of radio communication, ships exchanged messages by a code of light flashes. Light signals are still used today. Lighthouses warn ships of danger. Red lights often signal danger, for example a car's red brake lights warn others that it is slowing down. Traffic lights signal when to stop and when it is safe to go.

SOUND SIGNALS

Light travels faster than sound, so light signals are quicker, but they are no use if the person receiving the message is looking in the wrong direction. You cannot ignore sound, but it does not travel very far. Early humans sent messages by beating on drums or hollow logs. Today, bells still call people to church and telephones and doorbells ring for attention.

A relay system of postriders was used 2000 years ago in ancient Persia

POSTAL SERVICE

In ancient times, long communications were sent by runners, who carried the message inscribed on a clay tile. The famous Pony Express, a fast mail service run by relays of horseriders, operated in America for only a year. It ended in 1861 with the completion of the telegraph line. The postal service, as we think of it today, grew around the rail networks that sprang up in the nineteenth century. Airmail only began this century, though pigeons have been used for hundreds of years to carry messages.

EVERY FLAG TELLS A STORY

Flags are an important means of communication. People wave them to cheer on a sports team, celebrate a victory or show how proud they are of their country.

STANDARDS OF THE PAST

About 5000 years ago, the ancient Chinese, Indians and Egyptians put carved animals or other sacred objects on top of poles. These standards were used to show others who or what the bearers supported. Cloth flags were probably first flown in ancient China. By A.D. 1000, most European flags were cloth, though wooden standards were still popular.

FLAG DESIGNS

Designs on cloth developed with the Crusades. The Christian symbol of the cross was one of the earliest emblems. Today, every nation has its own flag, with a design that means something special to its nationals. For example the 13 stripes on the US flag represent each of the original colonies that formed the nation and there is one star for every state. Further stars are added for new states.

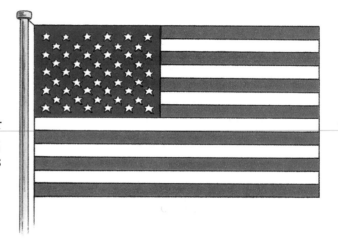

St George

St Andrew

St Patrick

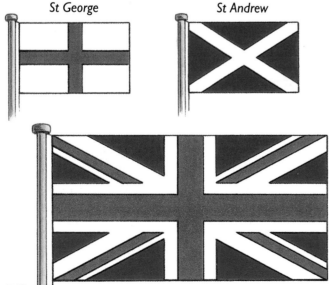

The British flag, the Union Jack, took its present form in 1801. It combines the national crosses of St George of England (red on a white field), St Andrew of Scotland (diagonal white on blue) and St Patrick of Ireland (diagonal red on white).

SEMAPHORE SIGNALS

In 1792, the French engineer Claude Chappé invented a semaphore system, but it did not use flags. He built towers to send messages. On top of each tower was a post with movable arms. The arm positions stood for letters and words and could be seen through a telescope from the next tower. A message could travel 100 kilometres in just a few minutes – on a clear day!

The flag semaphore alphabet uses just two flags. These are held in different positions to represent the 26 letters of the alphabet. This semaphore system is still used by naval signalmen.

INTERNATIONAL FLAG CODE

Another way to communicate by flag is to use the international code of signals. The code is made up of 26 different flags for the letters of the alphabet and triangular pennants for numbers. Sailors still hoist these flags to signal a message. They are shown on the next page. There is also a series of one-colour message flags which you can see below.

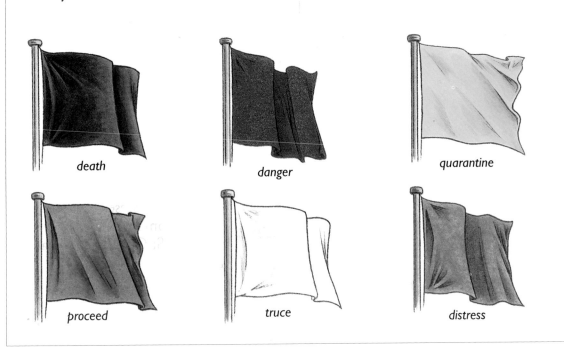

death

danger

quarantine

proceed

truce

distress

FLY THE FLAG

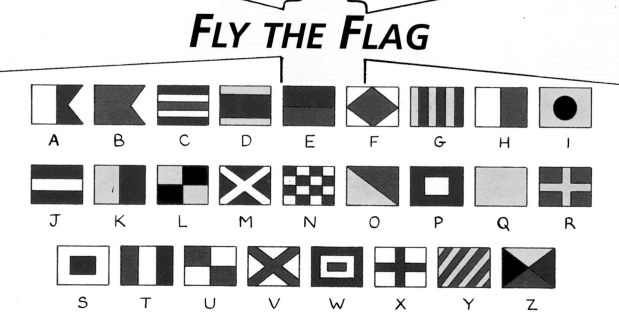

You could make your own set of code flags and send a message to a friend. The following instructions tell you how to make flag A. Follow the pictures to make the other letter flags.

FLAG 'A'

1. Draw a rectangle 17 x 16 cm on blue paper. Cut it out.

2. Make a fold 1 cm from the edge, to leave a 16 x 16 cm square.

▲ **3.** Cut two 16 x 8 cm strips of white paper and stick one strip over the folded edge. Turn the square over and stick the other strip in the same position, so the flag looks the same on both sides.

You will need:
- glue stick ● pencil ● ruler
- blue and white paper
- garden stick ● scissors

▲ **4.** Cut a triangle out of the blue paper, as shown.

5. Slot the flag on to the garden stick.

18

WRITE IT DOWN

Perhaps the most important invention in the history of communication was writing. People needed a written language in order to pass information on accurately.

PICTURES ON THE WALL

Writing grew out of picture making. Prehistoric cave-dwellers drew pictures of animals and objects on the walls of their shelters to record their experiences. Thousands of years later, these cave pictures tell us about our ancestors, the animals they hunted and the weapons and tools they used. Many paintings show animals that died out a long time ago.

An ancient cave painting from the Lascaux caves in France

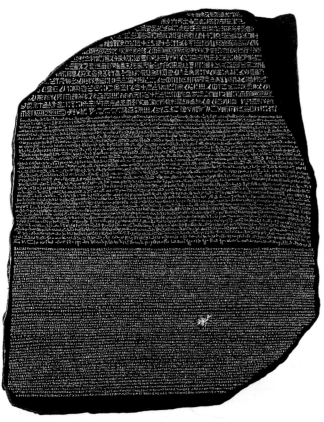

The Rosetta stone, found near the mouth of the Nile in 1799, was inscribed with the same message in three different writing systems – hieroglyphic, demotic and Greek. Because they understood Greek, scholars were able to decipher the Egyptian writing

PICTURE WRITING

Over 5000 years ago the people of Sumeria (present-day Iraq) developed a system of writing using pictures. Later, the ancient Egyptians wrote using a system of over 700 hieroglyphs. A hieroglyph was a picture which represented what it showed; for example, a wavy line meant water. Over time the hieroglyphs began to represent sounds instead.

SPEED WRITING

The Egyptians wrote on paper-like material called papyrus, using reed pens and ink. The scribes who did the writing developed a quicker system of joined-up hieroglyphs, called hieratic. Later, an even simpler form, called demotic, was used for everyday writing.

ALPHABETS

The earliest alphabet developed in Phoenicia, in the eastern Mediterranean, about 5000 years ago. The ancient Greeks borrowed the idea and, from Greece, it moved to Italy. There the alphabet was adapted first by the Etruscans and then by the Romans. With slight adaptations, the Roman alphabet is still used by most European languages, including English.

Other alphabets have more than 26 letters. Arabic has 28, and Russian 32.

Modern Chinese writing is still based on signs for ideas and objects. There are about 40,000 characters, and Chinese people have to learn about 4000 of these in order to write well.

WRITE YOUR NAME IN HIEROGLYPHS

Use this alphabet to write your name in ancient Egyptian hieroglyphs. Some sounds did not exist in the Egyptian alphabet, so you can make up your own hieroglyphs for them.

MASS COMMUNICATION

Communication was revolutionised by the invention of printing. It meant that knowledge could be stored in books and passed on from generation to generation.

THE FIRST PRINTERS

Over 1100 years ago, the Chinese invented a method of printing a whole page at a time, using carved blocks of wood and ink. Later they devised a way of putting separate characters together in lines. These skills were developed in Europe about 600 years later and, in about 1440, a German called Johannes Gutenberg started using movable metal type to print. This meant that individual letters could be printed rather than whole pages or lines of text.

Chinese wood block of an illustration

THE PRINTING PRESS

Gutenberg used a machine called a printing press to transfer inked letters on to a large sheet of paper. It meant that thousands of copies of a book could be printed in less time than it took a monk to write just one manuscript. At first many people were afraid of printed books, despite the fact that early printers mainly produced bibles and religious works. They gradually got used to them as they realized that they could use them to learn about new ideas and discoveries.

HOT OFF THE PRESS

In the early 19th century, the steam-powered printing press represented another step toward mass communication. Newspapers could be printed much more quickly. Since then there have been further improvements, and modern presses can print over a million pages an hour. With up-to-date laser technology, books, newspapers and magazines reach millions of people and help to keep them informed about the world.

Gutenberg's press

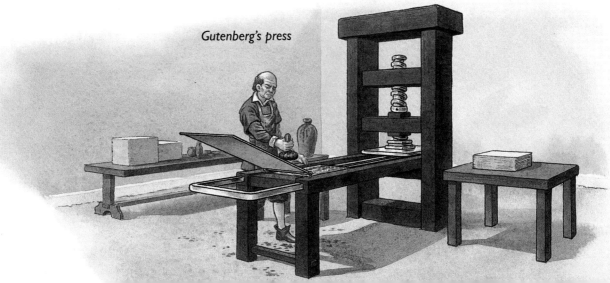

MAKE YOUR OWN BOOK

First decide what sort of book you want to make. It could be a story book, a joke book or an information book like the one shown here. Will you write the words, type them or print them from a computer? Would you like to illustrate the book yourself or use photographs?

We have used A4 sheets folded in half for the page size, but you might like to make a bigger book, especially if it has a lot of pictures. You can adapt the instructions to fit any shape or size.

PLANNING

1. Write an outline of all the main points to be included. This is called a synopsis. The title of this 24-page book is *Homes*.

1	Title page
2	Credits (names of helpers, sources of photographs, etc.)
3	Contents list
4	What is a home?
5	My house
6/7	Houses new and old
8	Animal homes
9	Fantasy houses
10/11	Homes on the move
12/13	Holiday homes
14	On stilts
15	In caves
16/17	The eco-house
18	The working house
19	Special needs
20/21	A future home
22/23	Design an ideal home
24	Glossary

You could make a practice book, called a dummy, by folding 12 pages in half and numbering them from 1 to 24. Then plan how to arrange the words and pictures on the pages. Book designers use a grid which is the same for every double-page spread.

You will need: ● ruler ● scissors ● card ● 6 A4 sheets of white paper ● 1 A4 sheet of coloured paper ● 2 pieces of card slightly larger than your pages (22 x 16 cm for A4) ● strong covering paper, 40 x 28 cm ● hessian, 10 x 29 cm ● paper ● glue ● needle and thread

THE BINDING

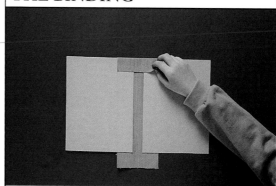

▲ **2.** Place the two pieces of card on the hessian, leaving a space of 2 cm in the middle. Glue the card to the hessian, fold the overlapping pieces over and stick down the ends.

THE COVER

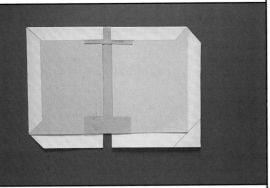

▲ **3.** For the cover, you could decorate some coloured paper. Allow 3 cm overlap all round. Cut off the corners and make a 2-cm slit at the top and bottom of the spine. Fold the cover paper over and stick down the edges.

THE PAGES

4. Fold the sheets, put them together and number the pages. Place the folded coloured sheet around the white pages. This will be the endpapers, which stay blank. Paste your text and illustrations to the pages.

STITCHING THE PAGES

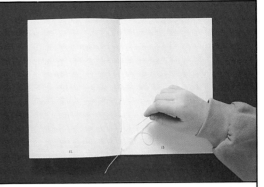

▲ **5.** Clip the pages together and mark the centrefold with 9 dots for the sewing holes. Pierce the holes with a needle before sewing them together with strong thread. Knot the ends tightly.

GLUING THE PAGES

6. Place the pages carefully on the middle of the cover, and stick the endpapers to the cover.

CODED MESSAGES

In 1838 the American inventor Samuel Morse discovered a clever way of using electricity to send messages. He designed a telegraph system which used a code in the form of short dots and long dashes. You will find how to make your own simple Morse system on pages 25-26.

MAKE A CIPHER WHEEL

You will need: ● card ● protractor ● ruler ● pencil ● pair of compasses ● paper fastener

▲ **1.** Use the pair of compasses to make two circles on card, 12 and 15 cm in diameter. Cut out the discs, and use a protractor to mark each with 36 segments of 10 degrees each. Write the letters A to Z and the numbers 0 to 9 in order on both discs.

2. Pin the discs together with a paper fastener.

3. To write your message in code, choose a key letter – say, G. Then turn the outer wheel until A lines up with the key letter on the inner wheel. Encipher your message by writing down the inner letters that correspond with the outer letters in your message. So, with key letter G, "YES" would be "5KY".

4. To decode the message, your friend sets his wheel to the same key letter and reads the corresponding letters off the outer wheel.

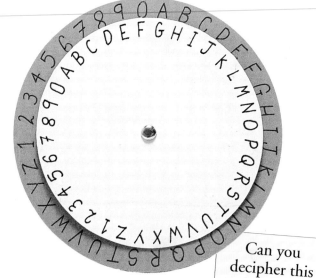

Can you decipher this message, with key letter G? MUUJR1IQ

Good luck

WIRED UP

In the 1870s Alexander Graham Bell invented the telephone. By 1891, a telephone line had been laid on the bed of the English Channel and Londoners could talk to Parisians. Telephone exchanges connected wires from a number of phones and calls were linked by operators. Many years later, telephone users could dial calls for themselves. In 1962, the first space satellite was used to bounce calls across the Atlantic.

MAKE YOUR OWN TELEGRAPH SYSTEM

Use this system to send messages in Morse code.

You will need: ● 4.5 volt battery with flat metal connection strips ● shoe-box lid ● low-voltage torch bulb ● tin foil ● low-voltage buzzer ● 70 cm double wire ● scissors ● glue ● empty light-bulb box ● 8 x 3 cm strip of cardboard ● big pin ● sticky tape ● black sugar paper ● Blu-tack

A	B	C	D	E	F	G
● ━	━ ● ● ●	━ ● ━ ●	━ ● ●	●	● ● ━ ●	━ ━ ●
H	**I**	**J**	**K**	**L**	**M**	**N**
● ● ● ●	● ●	● ━ ━ ━	━ ● ━	● ━ ● ●	━ ━	━ ●
O	**P**	**Q**	**R**	**S**	**T**	**U**
━ ━ ━	● ━ ━ ●	━ ━ ● ━	● ━ ●	● ● ●	━	● ● ━
V	**W**	**X**	**Y**	**Z**		
● ● ● ━	● ━ ━	━ ● ● ━	━ ● ━ ━	━ ━ ● ●		

THE WIRES

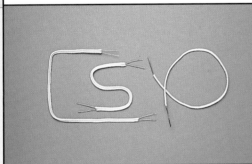

▲ **1.** Cut 2 lengths of wire 25 cm and 17 cm. Take another 25 cm of wire and split in half to make a single wire. Use sharp scissors to strip about 2 cm off the plastic covering from both ends of all three wires.

THE MORSE KEY

▲ **2.** Fold the strip of cardboard in half. Cut a 1-cm hole in the middle of the folded end. Stick a large piece of Blu-tack to the inside of the bottom and the top of the card strip.

COMPLETING THE CIRCUIT

3. Twist the stripped ends of the 25 cm long double wire around each other. Slot the wire through the hole in the Morse key, and press the ends into the Blu-tack on the bottom of the folded card strip. Cover the wires with a square piece of folded tin foil. Make sure the stripped ends touch the foil. Do the same with the 25 cm single wire, fitting it to the top part of the card strip.

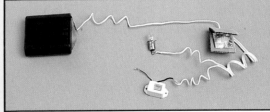

▲ **4.** Split about 8 cm of the other end of the double wire. Connect one separated end to the base of the bulb and the other separated end to the stripped buzzer wire. Secure all connections with sticky tape. Fasten the single wire to the long connecting strip of the battery with sticky tape.

25

5. Wrap the stripped ends of the 17 cm long double wire around the shorter connection strip of the battery and secure them with sticky tape. Split about 8 cm of the other end. Wrap one half around the bulb thread and join up the other half with the second buzzer wire. Secure all stripped wire connections with sticky tape.

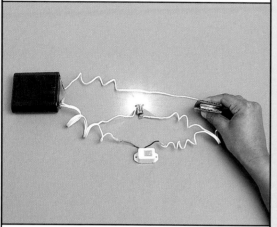

▲ Test the circuit by pressing the Morse key. All connections must be firmly fixed for it to work.

SETTING UP

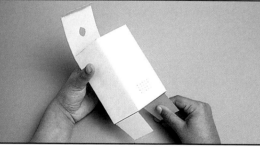

▲ **6.** Open the top flap of the light-bulb box and cut a small hole in the centre, big enough for the torch bulb to fit through. Cut away the top side flaps. Cut off the bottom flap, but keep the bottom side flaps. Pierce several holes into the front panel with a large needle, as an amplifier for the buzzer.

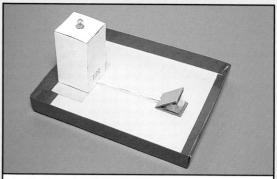

▲ **7.** Put the battery, buzzer and bulb into the box and push the bulb through the hole at the top. All the interconnecting wires should also be stored in the box. Press the Morse key to test the connections before gluing the light-box down. Put some glue on the bottom side flaps, and stick the box down at one end of the shoe-box lid. Tape down the double and single wires leading to the Morse key. Stick the key opposite the light box.

FINISHING TOUCHES

8. Cover the wiring with black sugar paper. Cut out holes for the light box and the Morse key and glue the paper into the lid. Flash and buzz your message down the wires. Hold the key down longer for a dash than for a dot.

ON A WAVELENGTH

Radio waves travel through the air at the speed of light, so a message can be sent almost instantaneously anywhere in the world. Radio waves can even travel through space to communicate with astronauts.

WIRELESS COMMUNICATION

In 1894, a 20-year-old Italian named Guglielmo Marconi built a transmitter with which he could send radio waves to a receiver. Since nothing connected the transmitter to the receiver, the invention was called the wireless. In 1901 Marconi broadcast a radio signal across the Atlantic Ocean. Long-distance communication has never been the same since. Radio became a vital link for ships and then aircraft. By the 1920s, regular public broadcasts were being successfully made in many countries. Suddenly people could keep in touch with the latest news in the comfort of their own homes.

VISION ON

But there was more to come, since radio waves can be used to transmit pictures as well as sound. In 1925, a British inventor called John Logie Baird sent a moving picture from one room in his house to another. The age of television had begun. Regular television broadcasts began in the 1940s and 1950s and, in 1962, live TV pictures were transmitted across the world via satellite. Modern colour TV sets are much more advanced than the small black-and-white sets of fifty years ago. Today television is the most popular form of mass communication in the world. Most countries have several channels broadcasting programmes virtually round the clock.

27

GETTING INTERACTIVE

Modern multimedia technology makes it possible to combine words, pictures, sound and graphics on a computer screen. The word multimedia means "many communications". Communication is becoming more interactive, which means that people can join in or "interact" with it.

COMPACT DISCS

In 1979 compact discs, or CDs, were introduced as a means of playing recorded music. Now CDs can store large amounts of information – graphics and text, as well as sound. In fact one 12 centimetre wide CD-ROM (**c**ompact **d**isc **r**ead **o**nly **m**emory) can store the equivalent of 300,000 pages of text. Any part of this information is accessed in seconds by a computer with a special disc drive and software. The user can interact with the system by using a hand control such as a computer mouse. This has all happened within the space of 15 years. Imagine what Samuel Morse or Guglielmo Marconi would think of it!

SUPERHIGHWAY INTO THE FUTURE

Today, thousands of kilometres of glass-fibre cables are being installed all over the world, creating what is known as the "data highway" or "information superhighway".

ELECTRONIC MAIL

Personal computers can be used to send information around the world. Your computer must be linked to the data highway, usually via the telephone system. The information you send is received on a computer at the other end.

This system of electronic mail, or e-mail, is very fast. In 1994 about 30 million people were using the system. In Japan, a glass-fibre system is planned to link almost every Japanese home and office by 2015.

FAST COMMUNICATION – ANYWHERE, AT ANY TIME!

A breakthrough in communications technology during the 1980s was the creation of the fax machine. Documents are sent down the telephone line and reproduced instantly at the receiver's end, but electronic mail users think this is too slow! People like to be constantly in touch, wherever they are, so communication is expected to be instantaneous. Mobile phones, using radio waves, make this possible.

THE FUTURE

Methods of communication may become even faster, easier and cheaper. Yet people still feel happiest talking to each other in person and their body language is as important as it ever was. People still write letters, read books – and even wave flags. Perhaps it will continue that way, with new technologies adding to the wealth of human communication.

In 1983, the Pioneer space probe became the first man-made object to leave our solar system. It carried a message from people on Earth, in case any other form of life should ever find the probe. Despite all our modern technology, this communication was in the form of a pictogram, showing a man and a woman, the spacecraft and the position of the planets. Universal communication needs to remain simple

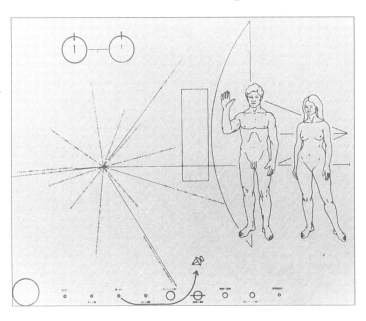

GLOSSARY

alphabet – a set of letters or other symbols used in a writing system, usually arranged in a special order.

beacon – a fire or light on a hill or tower that acts as a signal.

broadcast – to transmit by radio or television.

cipher – a method of secret writing by substituting letters according to a code.

circuit – a complete path through which an electric current can flow.

compact disc – a small digital disc carrying sound, text or graphics.

fax (facsimile) machine – a machine that sends and receives copies of documents down telephone lines.

hieroglyph – a simple picture representing an object or a sound.

interactive – allowing two-way communication between a user and a computer program.

laser – a device that turns light into an intense narrow beam.

mime – an art form using gestures and body movements to act out a story without using words.

mobile phone – a portable wireless telephone that uses radio waves.

multimedia – the combined use of words, pictures, sounds and graphics on a computer.

nerve cell – a cell that carries messages between the brain and other parts of the body.

semaphore – a signalling system using movable arms or flags to stand for letters and words.

sign language – a system of communication using hand signals or gestures.

space probe – an unmanned spacecraft that sends scientific information back to Earth.

superhighway – a network of glass-fibre cables that carries information between computers in people's offices and homes.

tattoo – a design on the skin made by pricking and staining with colour.

telegraph – a system by which information can be passed on using coded electrical signals.

telephone exchange – a place where telephone lines are connected and calls are put through by an operator.

RESOURCES

PLACES TO VISIT

Bath Postal Museum
8 Broad Street
Bath BA1 5LJ
Tel: 01225 460333
(Collection includes the history of
the post)

Horniman Museum
100 London Road
London SE23 3PQ
Tel: 0181 699 1872
(Ethnographic section includes material
illustrating man's beliefs, arts and crafts)

Museum of Mankind
6 Burlington Gardens
London W1X 2EX
Tel: 0171 437 2224
(Displays of ancient, recent and
contemporary life-styles of non-Western
societies)

Science Museum
Exhibition Road
London SW7 2DD
Tel: 0171 938 8123
(Historical collection showing the
development of communications to the
present day)

BOOKS TO READ

Animal Behaviour: Communication
by David Burnie (Watts Books)

Breakthrough: Communications
(Macdonald Young Books)

Communication Through the Ages by
Piero Ventura (Macdonald Young Books)

Exploring Technology: Communications
by Malcolm Dixon (Wayland)

Eyewitness Science: Electronics
(Dorling Kindersley)

Inventions: A Visual History by Richard Platt
(Dorling Kindersley)

New Technology: Communications
by Nigel Hawkes (Gloucester Press)

Pioneers of Science: Guglielmo Marconi
by Nina Morgan (Wayland)

Science Discovery: Communications
by Michael Jay (Wayland)

Stepping Through History: The Post
by Peggy Burns (Wayland)